THE ARK AT THE END OF THE GARDEN

The Ark at the End of the Garden

CHILDREN'S STORIES
FOR CHURCH AND HOME

by
RITA F. SNOWDEN

LONDON
THE EPWORTH PRESS

THE EPWORTH PRESS
(FRANK H. CUMBERS)
25-35 City Road, London, E.C.1.

MELBOURNE CAPE TOWN
NEW YORK TORONTO

SET IN MONOTYPE BASKERVILLE AND PRINTED IN
GREAT BRITAIN BY THE CAMELOT PRESS LTD
LONDON AND SOUTHAMPTON

In gratitude to all those
who lived these stories
before I wrote them

CONTENTS

THE ART OF THE STORY-TELLER . . . 9

1. THE ARK AT THE END OF THE GARDEN . . 17

2. THE BIG MAN AND THE LITTLE BEAR . . 20

3. LITTLE JANE'S DREAM 22

4. JOHNNY STIFFNECK 24

5. THE SECRET OF THE LITTLE TOWN . . 26

6. OUT OF THE MUD-HOLE 28

7. ALL THE LITTLE LIGHTS 30

8. THE TOFFEE MAN. 32

9. THE TEACHER WITH INFLUENZA . . . 34

10. THE CLEVER CROWS 36

11. THE MAN WHO NEVER FORGOT . . . 39

12. LITTLE ODD TOM 42

13. COCKY ROBERTS 45

14. THE SELFISH EMPRESS 47

15. BEGINNING AT BETHLEHEM 49

16. HOW COURAGE CAME TO THE PEOPLE . . 51

17. LITTLE SILVER BELLS 53

18. TIMOTHY'S DREAM 55

19. THE LAND OF THE LITTLE WOVEN BASKET . 57

20. MR ANONYMOUS 60

21. TOP OF THE WORLD 62

22. SWEETHEART ABBEY 64

23. TWO EYES, THREE EYES 66

24. FOLLOW MY LEADER 68

25. WHAT HAPPENED TO THE PEOPLE OF ONO . 70

26. THE MAN WHO STOOD UP TO THINGS . . 72

27. THE LIFE-BOAT MEN 75

28. THE OLD PARSON'S PUDDING . . . 77

29. KNOCKING AT THE DOOR OF THE LITTLE HOUSE 79

30. THE YOUNG DISCOVERER 81

31. CHARLIE'S TREES 83

[These first few pages are for grown ups. Boys and girls who read this book for themselves can skip them and begin with the stories.]

THE ART OF THE STORY-TELLER

WHO loves stories? Just about everyone. Try telling them and see.

Some of us are natural story-tellers, just as some of us are natural singers, and some are natural cooks; but most of us have to learn, and most of us learn by trial and error. There are, nevertheless, some general rules. Of set purpose there are no Bible stories in this book, although I shall make reference to them in this introduction.

The first requirement is a *lively desire*—to sing, to cook, to tell stories. The story-teller is assured of his place in every heart. 'The most beautiful thing in the world to me', says Charles Laughton, the British actor, 'is a sea of faces listening to a story.' John Masefield, Poet Laureate, speaks of 'children to whom lovely stories are as necessary as pure air. I have seen', he says, 'the hunger of the young for stories; it is a hunger.'

So when you and I tell stories, we are not doing something unnatural, like raising pineapples in Greenland; we are doing something very close to nature.

Next it is important to take *the age of one's group* into consideration. The poet speaks of stories that 'will hold children from their play, and old men from the chimney-corner.' Obviously, they will not be the same stories—or if they are, they will not be told in the same way. Even among the children, there will be different needs; and those needs will be largely governed by age.

Earliest in the story age comes what I call the *Realistic Period*. Life at this stage centres totally in the things one's tiny listeners know—home, mother, father, meals, beds, babies, pussies, and the like. It is not a big world, but it is a very real world. And it must be entered and dealt with tenderly.

There are plenty of stories in the Bible that can be simplified for this age group—stories of the baby Moses sleeping in his little basket; the Baby Jesus in the manger, and the beautiful star shining over Him; Mary making the bread and mending the clothes; father Joseph sawing off little play-blocks from pieces of wood at his bench. And there are the simple settings of many of the stories Jesus Himself told—of the mother-hen gathering her chickens under her wing when the storm comes; of the lady who lost her little coin, and took up all her mats, and swept her house to find it; and the kind shepherd who lost his sheep, and the good father who lost his boy.

Next comes the *Imaginative Period* when our listeners are daily enjoying wonderful 'make-ups', and telling them, often to the confusion of big people; not lies, but make-ups. They have no difficulty in hunting lions at the end of the garden, or in believing that 'the mountains and hills break forth into singing', that trees and birds talk, and that houses have feelings very much like their own. My little friend, Paul, who sends me stories through the post— in large pencilled words, three or four to the line—belongs to this period. In a recent effort he began: 'Once upon a time a little house stood on a hill. It was very tired standing in the same place all day . . .' Then he told of some people who came by, and what the little house said to them. It is quite easy for little houses to feel all sorts of things, and to say all sorts of things, at this stage.

No clear line, of course, is visible between one period and the next—they merge, with some a little earlier, with others a little later—but our listeners will progress through each in time.

After the Imaginative Period comes the *Heroic Period*. This is the age when our listeners are more interested in what people *do* than in what they say, when, above all, they want stories of people who do things, stories of

courage, of daring, of action. The great secret is to plunge
your story into action at once, and to get your characters
doing things; don't waste a lot of time describing them.
Have you noticed the stories told by Jesus, in this respect?
Take His best-known story of the prodigal son. The Great
Story-teller doesn't risk inattention by telling us what the
characters are like. He plunges them straight into action.
'A certain man had two sons.' In that, the characters are
introduced, and we want to hear what is going to happen
to them. And we hear it at once: 'The younger son said,
"Father, give me the portion of goods that falleth to me".
And he divided unto them his living.' And on it goes,
a fast-moving succession of actions, until the party of
rejoicing at the end, where we are left with the highly
satisfactory impression that they 'lived happily ever
after'.

The Bible from cover to cover is rich in stories of this
kind—stories of action: David with his little sling and
handful of stones, squaring up to the giant; Nehemiah,
the King's cup-bearer, organizing his men and materials
to build the city; Elijah standing up to the false priests of
Baal, shouting his challenge on Carmel; and the New
Testament missionary stories, following on the stories of
Jesus.

Stories of saints, and of explorers and road-makers and
missionary pioneers serve here; and so, too, do modern
stories of scientists and of servants of the people, such as
Dr Schweitzer in his hospital in the Primeval Forest,
Kagawa going to live among the poor people of the
slums, Jane Addams the good neighbour of Hull House,
the Curies discovering radium, and Dr Fleming discovering penicillin. In addition there are fine sports characters.
Such heroes, at this age, kindle imagination. There are
the splendid conquerors of the great white spaces—Dr
Edward Wilson of the Antarctic, and Captain Scott; Dr
Howard Somervell who made an attempt on Everest, and
Sir Edmund Hillary who conquered that mighty peak.

A little later—in the teens—comes as naturally the

Romantic Period. For this there are the stories of great friendships between characters of the opposite sex and of the same sex, such as David and Jonathan, or Ruth and Naomi. Lives of musicians, of artists, and of statesmen are rich in material too whenever they show us high ideals: loyalty and courage, a battle to be won, a tenderness to be matched with strength and love.

These, in a general sense, are the four periods of growth, of which every story-teller must take notice.

Now a few general things about the story. Either you can re-tell other people's stories, or you can make your own. You will probably want to do both, so you will need one folder to collect stories, and another for the cuttings and notes on which stories will be based.

A good story is an artistic offering, like a poem written or recited; or a piece of music, composed or performed. It may seem the easiest thing in the world, but behind it will be hours and days of preparation and practice. Don't think you can do it without effort. You can't. You might manage once to tell a good story right out of your imagination, and on the spur of the moment; but you can't hope to keep it up. Not unless you are a genius. You must prepare and practise.

The first thing is *Choose your Story*. It is fun to have a new one, but old ones can be told and re-told, if they are loved. But there comes a time when—if we can go by the little girl whose teacher too often returned to Genesis—the old ones need a rest. Said the little girl: 'I'm tired of the story of the Adamses.'

Of course, it depends how realistically it is done. 'A Bible story read by my mother', said Hugh Redwood, 'was like a good steel engraving; but Annie our maid (Annie was chapel, we were church) read in gorgeous Technicolor, so that I saw the yellow dust rise behind the camels of Abraham's servant, and feasted my eyes on Rebekah's bright attire and beauty as she came with the women of Nahor to the well in the sunshine of late afternoon. That, for some reason, was one of my favourite

Bible pictures. . . .' We all have our favourites. But a great deal depends on how graphically a story is told; and that goes for any age group, even those beyond the four we have examined. Dr Sangster, speaking to preachers in *The Craft of Sermon Construction*, says: 'Read Alexander Whyte describing the man who knocked at midnight, and asked for three loaves. It is not, in its wholeness, a picture sermon, but it begins that way. You *see* the man. You see him wait between his knocks. You see him turn to go home . . . and then turn back again. You hear the dogs bark at this midnight hammering. You see him put his ear to the door and then his eye to the hole. . . . Read it slowly once, and the man who knocked at the door will be for ever real to you. The picture drawn by our Lord in two or three deft strokes has been filled out for you, pulled into clear focus, and cast on a white screen. You have only to shut your eyes and you can see it.'

Now how is it that the man is real to us? It is because the story-teller has himself first had a clear vision of him. This is a very important point; you must visualize your story happening, before ever you attempt to tell it. Almost anyone can tell what he has seen—a bird building in the plum-tree, an accident in the playground—and the characters and sequence of events in your story must be just as clear as if you were an eye-witness. Get the facts of the story clearly in your mind, and then, casting books and lesson-helps aside, relax in a chair, close your eyes, and see the whole thing happening. It will give you confidence; you won't hesitate, because you won't be bothered with books or lesson-papers that come between you and your listeners; and you will be able to use your own words, which are always better than other people's, even if they are not quite so picturesque.

And may I say a few words about words? It is always important to use simple words—words familiar to the child. My Scottish teacher friend told me—as we journeyed round a loch—of a child who described Elisha as 'the prophet who took the widow for a cruise'. Obviously he was not familiar with the word 'cruse' as applied to a pot or an earthenware jar.

It is just as important to make sure that words are clearly said. There is no need to use slang; it doesn't serve you, and children don't expect it.

Another thing is to get your facts right, so that a child need never re-learn later what your story has told him. Even if the story is imaginary, it must be consistent; if it is a religious story—a story of God's dealing with some character—it must be consistent with what we know of God, in Jesus Christ. Where an odd idea is held in the Old Testament, we must say that it was held before Jesus came, when men and women didn't know very much about God. And you must keep your characterization consistent, so that Peter, for instance, a fisherman and an impulsive fellow, a blusterer rugged and strong, acts that way all through. If you are making up a story out of gathered facts, you will clothe them with the fascinating garments of your imagination, but you must not allow the finished story to go against the facts.

The beginning of the story is important, and so, too, is the ending. I would even go so far as to suggest that you write out clearly, and memorize, your beginning and your ending. If you can get away to a crisp, clear start, especially if you are new at story-telling, you will not take fright at the sound of your own voice; and you will have a chance of rapt attention from the very start.

Don't begin your story till everyone is quiet. To wait a second or two, looking your company in the face, is a good way to get the atmosphere ready. And, of course, you will see that everyone is comfortable, and that each listener can look into your face as the story proceeds.

You will vary your speed and tone—starting softly and slowly, perhaps, or excited and eagerly, as the action of the story seems to suggest. A voice without modulation becomes dull.

Use direct speech as often as you can, and put it into the mouths of your characters. Jesus did. In His great story of the Prodigal, He made His character say: 'Father, give me the portion of goods that falleth to me. . . .' And again: 'I will arise, and go unto my father. . . .' Children, as well as big people, understand this kind of speech; they use it in their play, and in their conversation. Do a little eavesdropping, and you will be persuaded of this.

Give your characters names—children like names. They don't understand anonymous acts, any more than some of us understand anonymous letters. But be careful not to name too many characters, or to introduce well-known names used in another connexion, lest confusion results. From beginning to end it must be easy to keep one's eye on the hero.

If you have to tell a well-known story—such as the Bible stories that recur at Christmas, Easter, and Whitsuntide—it is easy to give them freshness by telling them from a new angle. The Christmas Story can be told, for instance, from the viewpoint of the innkeeper. So it will begin at the point where he answers the knock of two weary, dust-covered travellers who come to his door. He has already answered it more often than he can remember; he is confused and worried, and tired with all the fuss of folk coming and going. You must find out, by a little research, what his inn was like; how far the travellers had come; where they would sleep, where they would tie up their donkey, what kind of smells of cooking there would be, and what kinds of noise. And this, as one angle only, must be consistent with the whole story as we know it recorded in Scripture.

Don't overcrowd your story with ideas; one good, clear, central idea is enough at a time.

The story should not leave your listener with a lot of jagged, unsatisfactory ends. A child cannot easily bear a sense of calamity. If you have to tell the story of Good Friday to very little children, take care to reduce as much as possible the harrowing details, and link the whole sad event with the 'happy ending', the triumph of Easter Day.

As for your story's moral: there are three possibilities, and you must decide which is best for the story you are telling. The Master Story-teller varied His method. You can likewise leave the moral *implicit* in the story; you can *underline* it; you can *tack it on at the end*. In the story Jesus told of the Prodigal the moral is implicit in the story; it is of the very structure of it. In His story of the Sower, it is underlined: 'His disciples asked Him, saying, "What might this parable be?" And He said, "Now the parable is this: The Seed is the Word of God. . . ."' and so on. In His story of the Good Samaritan, He uses the third method, that of pointing the moral at the end. To His listeners He said: 'Go, and do thou likewise.' Don't let anyone persuade you there is only one way to tell a story.

You will soon find there is great interest and happiness in the art; and in time you will agree with Charles Laughton: 'The most beautiful thing in the world is a sea of faces listening to a story.'

R. F. S.

THE ARK AT THE END OF THE GARDEN

IN the Morton family there were only two boys; Benny and John. But down the road there were two other families; the Shaws and the Stewarts. That made seven boys and girls altogether. They didn't see much of each other in term-time, because Benny and John and the Stewart boys went to different schools, and the two small Shaw girls to boarding-school.

But in the holidays they had great fun together. At the back of the Morton's house there was a fine playing-ground, and for when it rained an old disused workshop that they called 'The Ark'. It had a gabled roof, with a tiny high window, which Benny said made it look just like the real Ark. And since they never went there save when the rain was pouring down, it seemed fitting. It was Benny who first gave the old workshop its name, and ever afterwards no one thought of calling it anything else.

Mrs Morton said that when they all got in together, it sounded like a lot of jabbering monkeys. But, on second thoughts, she remembered they weren't all monkeys in the Ark.

And that's where the trouble really began. On the first rainy day it was all right; it was good fun. But when the rain continued, somehow it didn't seem such good fun. When those who wanted to play snakes-and-ladders— a very suitable game to play in 'The Ark', when you come to think of it—found their game-board upset, they were sure to be annoyed. And somebody else in the middle of a good story was sure to be annoyed when the rest of the company made such a din that his head ached. And that was all very awkward, and used up a lot of patience. But when the rain kept on for a third and a fourth day things became even worse.

B

And then Benny suddenly got an idea. He had been puzzling his head to think what Mr Noah had done in the real Ark. He couldn't think how he had managed, until he came across a notice that somebody had imagined he must have put up in the Ark. And when Benny wakened up in the morning and found it still raining, he decided to borrow the idea of the notice.

So tearing out a large sheet of paper, he prepared it, and hammered it up on the door. And it was in such plain language that there was no one, not even the very smallest, who couldn't read it, and what was more, understand it. It said:

'Parrots, moderate your language. Elephants, mind where you tread, and avoid other people's corns. Hyenas, remember others want to sleep at night. Hens, don't fuss too much when you lay eggs. Cockerels, be sure it is dawn you greet, and not moonlight. Donkeys, try to be reasonable. Giraffes, keep your long necks out of other folk's business. Fishes and other water-loving creatures, leave room for somebody else sometimes. *All curb your odd ways and we shall manage.*' That last sentence—in clear letters like all the rest—was underlined.

The notice caused a lot of fun, but it made a difference. One by one, the inmates of 'The Ark' began to wonder whether perhaps he or she had not been a little selfish.

The notice, of course, was never meant for big people to see; but that night a wind sprang up, and Mr Morton heard a door banging somewhere. Wondering if it might not be the door of 'The Ark', he went down to see. And there was the notice.

At first, as he read it by the light of his torch, he laughed. Then he said, 'Jolly good idea! I must remember this. What a pity it can't be pinned up in every place where children play on rainy days—and where big people work any day—and where the nations of the world quarrel and make wars.' The only trouble, of course, was to think of a way to do it.

In the meantime, the notice—all through term-time

and holiday-time—still hangs up in 'The Ark', where the children come to play: 'Parrots, moderate your language. Elephants, mind where you tread, and avoid other people's corns. Hyenas, remember others want to sleep at night. Hens, don't fuss too much when you lay eggs. Cockerels, be sure it is dawn you greet, and not moonlight. Donkeys, try to be reasonable. Giraffes, keep your long necks out of other folk's business. Fishes and other water-loving creatures, leave room for somebody else sometimes. *All curb your odd ways, and we shall manage!*'

THE BIG MAN AND THE LITTLE BEAR

ONCE upon a time, a Dutch family settled in America. They had sons and daughters who married and had sons and daughters, and they married and had sons and daughters.

At last one of the sons of that family became President of the United States of America. His name was Theodore Roosevelt.

He was a big man, and a good man, and he had lots of energy. He led his people in ways of peace, and they trusted him. In his spare time he liked to travel and meet people. He liked to read books—and to write them. And he liked to go hunting in the woods.

One day when he was hunting in the woods he came suddenly on a little bear. It was a very little bear, and the huntsman's dogs, standing yapping on either side of it, made it look smaller than ever. It was just a baby bear, and it was frightened. It knew it couldn't get away.

When President Theodore Roosevelt—whom his friends called Teddy, for a nickname—saw the little bear, he called off the dogs, and stood by to guard it, until it could run away back into the woods.

And it ran away, and was soon safe.

But those who saw the big man and the little bear, suddenly began to laugh. He looked so big, and the little bear looked so small—but most of all they laughed at a hunter with a gun letting anything get away that he might have shot. They did not understand the kind of mercy in the heart of their big President, and when they got out of the woods, and back to where newspapermen worked, they told them the story. They laughed, in a hard, unfeeling way at what they called the President's weakness.

'Fancy,' they said, 'he could have shot it easily—and he let it get away.' And they laughed again.

Then they got one of the cartoonists—one of those clever men who draw funny pictures for the papers—to draw a picture of the big man, President 'Teddy' Roosevelt, with a gun in hand, turning his dogs off the little bear to allow it to go back into the woods. And lots of people who saw it in the paper laughed too. But lots didn't, because they knew what mercy was, and how important it was. They had read in their Bible this wonderful thing: 'What doth the Lord require of thee, but to do justly, and to love mercy, and to walk humbly with thy God' (Micah 6[8]).

Just about that time, the toy shops all over the land were beginning to sell little toy bears for children to play with. They were cosy, friendly little bears—but they hadn't a name for them. So when they heard the story of the President—'Teddy' Roosevelt—and the little bear in the woods, they called them 'Teddy-bears'. And Teddy-bears they have been ever since.

Perhaps you have a Teddy-bear of your own. Now it will seem to you nicer than ever, because it is a reminder of a big man whose heart was big enough to show mercy.

LITTLE JANE'S DREAM

LITTLE Jane Addams loved to walk holding her father's hand. And one day she walked with him through the poor, shabby streets of Freeport. Suddenly she gave his safe, strong hand a little tug, and next moment he was looking down into her grey-blue eyes. 'When I'm a grown-up lady', she said, 'I'm going to live in a great big house. And I'm going to have it right next door to poor people, so that their children can play in my yard.'

'Really', said her Quaker father. Then it slipped completely out of his thoughts, for it seemed nothing more than the dream of a little girl with grey-blue eyes.

But Jane did not forget it so easily; indeed, she never forgot it. And twenty years later, along with a college friend, she rented just such a house, for just such a purpose. The old house had been a mansion, and stood on Halstead Street, on Chicago's West Side. There were many people all around it, living crowded to overflowing in shabby houses. Some of them were Italian, some Swiss, some German, some French, some Russian, some Polish, some Irish. In all, they came from twenty-eight countries—most of them were poor, and most had nowhere for their children to play.

By this time, Jane had finished school and college and had travelled in many countries. A college friend—Ellen Starr Gates—had travelled with her, and bit by bit Miss Jane had shared her dream—a dream that had been growing ever since that far-away day when she had walked as a little girl with her father.

And one September night in 1889 her dream came true. With Miss Ellen, and another, Jane Addams moved into 'T'ole Hull House'.

It took lots of work to make it nice. It had been used as a storage place by a furniture factory, and there were worn floors and knocked walls to mend. It was hard work, scraping off ugly paint, and scrubbing and polishing. Then they brought pictures and vases and nice things from their own homes. And since they wanted to have music and singing, they saved up to buy a piano.

At last the day came when Hull House threw open its doors in welcome to any who cared to come. Jane Addams wanted just to be a good neighbour—and the little children, and the sad and lonely people, soon knew that her welcome was real. They saw that she really wanted to help them, and that she wanted to help them to help themselves. One of the things she did was to help clean up their horrid garbage-tins, that stood in alleys, inviting rats and sickness. It was a nasty job, but she kept at it till it was done—day after day, month after month.

At night, when she came back to Hull House, she plunged into a lovely hot bath. Then, in her nicest, prettiest clothes, she led the fun of the evening. She taught the people to sing, she taught them to pray, she taught them to do all sorts of things together, until the Italians who came along with the others found a new name for the old house—they called it The House of God (*la Casa di Dio*). And that was a good name for that happy place full of love and friendship, because all were welcome there, and learned to share there, no matter what country they came from, as brothers and sisters under God their great Father.

Before she died, an old woman with thousands and thousands of friends, and a happy song in her heart, Jane Addams was given a great honour—a half share in the Nobel Peace Prize.

But best of all now, everybody right round the world loves to hear the story of the old shabby house that was changed by love into The House of God.

JOHNNY STIFFNECK

JOHNNY STIFFNECK was a giraffe. He stood as high as three men, and he could pick his breakfast off the top of a tree, without any difficulty. He had such a long neck, though it had only seven bones in it. (Samuel Butler—a famous writer who said lots of funny things—said once, 'A giraffe must get up at six in the morning, if it wants to have its breakfast in its stomach by nine.' That was his amusing way of saying that a giraffe's neck is so long that it takes a long while for his breakfast to get from his mouth to his stomach.)

And there was another thing about Johnny Stiffneck that was awkward. His neck was so stiff. His meals were mostly tender green leaves from the tops of trees; but when he wanted to have a little change, and eat some nice juicy grass, he had the hardest job in the world to get down to it. And the same was true when he wanted to have a drink—it was such a bother, although his neck was so long. He had to stand by the water, with his legs as far apart as they would go, before he could get down to it. The trouble was that he was such a stiff-necked fellow.

Johnny Stiffneck lived in Abyssinia—and was captured. And the day came when he was to be transported to Europe to a fine zoo.

The first problem, of course, was how to get him there. In the end, it was decided to put him in a railway-truck—which seemed a fine, sensible idea—because a railway ran down from the capital, Addis Ababa, to the coast, where he could be put on a ship. But the trouble about it was that on that piece of railway there were a good many tunnels. When Johnny Stiffneck stood up in his truck, his long neck lifted his head much, much higher than the tunnel entrances. And being a stiffnecked fellow, he refused to do anything about it. But it was plain to everybody that unless somebody did something about it he would come to grief. And since no zoo in Europe would want a giraffe with his head knocked off, those responsible for getting him there set to work on an idea of their own.

They fixed a windlass to the front of his truck—a windlass is a winding machine with a handle and a fine strong piece of rope attached—and they fastened the rope to Johnny Stiffneck's head. He didn't like the idea very much, but by winding it carefully and slowly, they managed to get his head down.

Then the train started off. And every time the driver saw a tunnel ahead, he gave three hoots on his engine whistle, and the man in the truck along with Johnny Stiffneck got busy with the windlass. And in this way, they eventually got safely to the coast—and Johnny Stiffneck crossed by boat to Europe, and came safely to his zoo.

In the Bible, God speaks of His chosen people, the Israelites, as being like Johnny Stiffneck. He says: 'I have seen this people, and behold it is a stiff-necked people' (Deuteronomy 9¹³). He didn't mean, of course, that they had seven bones in their necks, so that they could pick leaves off the tops of the trees—no; He meant that they were a proud and stubborn people—so proud and stubborn that they held their heads high and were determined not to bow them, even to God.

And that wasn't good at all. So God had to send them many sorrows to bring them low. He had to let their enemies overcome them and carry them away into a strange land as captives. And at last they learned their lesson—and bowed their heads humbly to God. And thereafter, of course, like Johnny Stiffneck, they managed to get through life a lot better.

It doesn't do to be proud and stubborn—it is better to bow your head humbly, than to get it knocked off, isn't it?

THE SECRET OF THE LITTLE TOWN

ONCE, in the ancient, sunny land of Italy, Mr Hersey tells us, there stood a little town called Andano. It was a very little town, but the people who live in it—the men and women and boys and girls—loved it. It was theirs, and they knew each other, and they were very happy.

Then one day it was all changed. War had come—and war always changes things. And lots of their people were killed—which was very sad—and lots of their buildings were battered down.

After a while, when the battles were at an end, the American army sent some of its soldiers to live in the little town to keep the enemy from coming back, and to help the poor sad people to build up their town again. The soldier in charge of them was called Major Joppolo.

It was a big task, and first of all Major Joppolo sat in his office in the ancient Town Hall and thought and thought. Then he began to make plans. He had seen what had happened to Andano. And it seemed to him a good idea to show himself friendly to the people, and to ask them one by one what they felt would be the first and best thing to do. So he called them in one by one. 'What does this town need most, right now?' he asked.

Some answered him straight away: 'Food—we need food.'

Others said: 'No, we need cigarettes and sweets.'

Others clamoured for other things.

But there was one called Cacopardo who said: 'No.' And at first his answer rather puzzled the Major. 'What this town needs first of all', said he, 'is a bell—it needs a bell.'

When the people were hungry, and their houses were

broken down, and they hadn't had any sweets for a long time, Major Joppolo couldn't think why they should want a bell. But he was patient, and he set about finding out. He sent out and had the priest who preached and ministered to the people brought in.

Soon he learned that the bell that had hung so long in the little town had been carried off by the enemy and melted down to make weapons. And soon Major Joppolo learned of its importance. 'This bell', said the friendly priest who preached and ministered to the people, 'was the centre of the town. All life revolved around it. The farmers in the country were wakened by it in the morning, the drivers of the carts knew when to start by it, the bakers baked by it, even we in the churches depended on that bell more than our own bells. At noon on the Sabbath, when all the bells in the town rang at once, this bell rose above all the others, and that was the one you listened to.'

At last, Major Joppolo saw the matter clearly—the people of Andano were bewildered because they had lost the bell that gave direction to their lives. And he saw very clearly that nothing would come right in the little town, until they had another bell. And so at once he set about planning how to get a new bell for Andano.

Food and houses and sweets and cigarettes were well enough, but they were not the most important thing—the most important thing was a bell, so that their lives could be regulated.

And that is what the New Testament means in that lovely chapter, 1 Corinthians 13, that you have perhaps learned off by heart. You remember how it finishes. It has been talking about a number of good things: faith and hope—but it ends like this: 'and now abideth Faith, Hope, and Love, these three; *but the greatest of these is Love.*'

Exactly! And it's easier to understand it when we know the story of the people of Andano. For in our lives, Love is the bell that sets the note for everything else.

OUT OF THE MUD-HOLE

YOUNG Sam Meharry—his father called him Samuel—
was sixteen when he set out to make his fortune. News
reached him from the great West, and he piled his wagon
high with supplies, and set out. (The year was 1860, but
Sam was too eager to take much notice.)

All went well with Sam, until one afternoon in Indiana
his wagon stuck in a mud-hole. It was a very deep mud-
hole on a poorly formed track. And try as he could, Sam
couldn't get it out. The more he tried, the deeper the
wheels sank. And it was getting dark.

Soon he noticed through the darkness a tiny light
coming from a cabin door. It was a poor little cabin, but
soon he was knocking at its door. The friendly Negro who
answered it was a little surprised to see a white youth, but
when he saw how bespattered with mud he was, and how
tired, he asked him in. Then Sam told him of his wagon
in the mud-hole.

'Sure, I'll help you', said the kindly Negro, 'but I don't
think we can do it tonight. You better come in and have
some supper, and we'll 'tend to it in the mornin'.'

Sam's new-found friends were poor folks; they hadn't
much to share. But what they had, they shared gladly.
Soon Sam was sitting up to their table. When it came
time to go to bed, the friendly Negro said: 'You're in a
God-fearin' home, no harm will come to you. You can
lie down on the bes' pallet, and you can sleep sound.'

And Sam did sleep sound. He was tired after struggling
with his wagon. Soon after sunrise next morning, Sam
had a simple breakfast, and afterwards went out with his
new friend to the wagon. It was as firmly stuck as ever,
but as they scraped at the mud, and pushed and shoved

together, it gradually came out. Sam was very thankful.

'Now', said the Negro, 'whip up yoh mules, and get on yoh way.' And Sam did. But before he moved off, he called down: 'Thank you, good neighbour. If ever I grow rich out West, I'll remember you and your people. Good-bye!'

And Sam moved out of sight in his wagon.

But he never saw that man again. He couldn't even find where his little cabin stood. But he did not forget.

Sixteen years later—grown rich as he had hoped—Sam walked one day along the streets of Nashville, Tennessee, where there were lots of Negro people. He saw that most were poor, and some were very sick, and as he looked at them his heart was touched, and he remembered the kindly Negro who had come to his aid when he was in trouble.

There and then he made up his mind. 'I will start a new school here', he said. 'And I will have young Negro men and women taught how to be good doctors and nurses. And I will persuade my brothers to help, and together we will get others to come and teach. We will build a great hospital to the glory of God, the great Father of us all, whether our skins are black or white.'

And he did. Four Meharry brothers joined in; and the Hubbard brothers; and the Methodist Church people helped, finding more money and more people with willing hearts, and in time one of the very finest medical colleges in the land was raised at Nashville. And there it is to this day—and it all started long ago at a mud-hole, where a young white man and a kindly black man worked together side by side as brothers.

ALL THE LITTLE LIGHTS

YEAR by year for Indian boys and girls and their parents who live in the Punjab comes a beautiful festival. It comes when the hot sticky nights of the monsoon have given place to the long pleasant evenings before the coming of the cold nights of winter.

It is called the Festival of Diwali (Dewalee), the festival of light.

At once all the housewives are busy preparing their homes for the families to sleep indoors, instead of out. The walls are given a new plaster to freshen them up, and then redecorated with colourful drawings.

But that is not all. As the evening of Diwali draws on, the housewives take hundreds of little earthenware saucers, and fill each with a few drops of linseed-oil. Then they twist little pieces of cotton wool into wicks, and place them in the saucers, and set them alight. With these hundreds of tiny lights, their homes are outlined against the dark velvety night. And what a pretty sight!

To go down into a bazaar on Diwali night is just like walking into fairyland. All the houses have their little lights, and so, too, do all the shops, against the warm Indian night.

As you walk along you are sure to wonder how it is that a light so tiny can continue to burn so brightly.

But there is a secret. Look more closely and you will see, behind the lights, a man standing with a tin of oil in his hands. He moves quietly up and down the rows of lights, and wherever he sees one beginning to flicker, he pours in a few more drops of oil, so that its little light is replenished and it can continue to burn brightly against the dark of the night.

And that's a wonderful secret. That is what Jesus does for us, His children. He calls us to let our lives shine like little lights in the world—and we try to do it. But we soon find that we cannot keep it up by ourselves. All the time—through prayer, Bible-reading, and worship, through the beauty of the world, and the love of those about us—He must stand close to our lives, to replenish them so that they can keep shining brightly and clearly. Without Him they would soon flicker, and that would be very sad.

But with Him, each of us can shine as brightly as a little light in the Festival of Diwali.

THE TOFFEE MAN

WHAT are the sweetest things in the world? Toffees? No, Lord Mackintosh of Halifax says: 'No!' And he has thousands of people working for him, making toffees in tons, and he has been making them all his life—and his father before him. Even before that, his mother made toffees—Mackintosh toffees—though, of course, she didn't make them in tons. That was a long, long time ago, and she made them in her ten-pound copper jam-pan, which had been one of her few wedding presents. But from that small beginning has gradually grown the tons and tons of toffees that are made every week—yes, every week. Can you imagine 500 *tons* of toffees all piled up in a heap? It sounds like a boy's dream, or a girl's dream, doesn't it?

But Lord Mackintosh of Halifax has sweeter memories, and he spoke of them a little while ago. His friends gave him a special dinner, at which many speeches were made. It was to celebrate his being raised to the peerage—being made a lord, by the Queen, for his services to the realm. For he does lots of good things besides making toffees— like being the World President of the Sunday School Association. Besides, he collects beautiful things, and he has a great many in his home to share with his friends.

When he was made a lord, he chose to be called Lord Mackintosh of Halifax—because his name was Mackintosh, and he came from Halifax. And when his friends gave him that special dinner, he said something lovely about his old mother—for his memories of his mother, and of his wife, are the two sweetest things in the world to him.

'When my mother died', he said, 'we found a little cardboard box. In it were a photo of father when they first met, which none of us had seen; the original toffee recipe, written in her own handwriting on the page of an exercise-book; and a letter thanking her for her work as a Sunday-school teacher. These', he added, 'were evidently her real treasures.'

And what are his? Well, after his mother, comes his wife. 'Every page of my scrap-book of memory', he said, 'is lit up by her presence and her smile.'

It adds to the sweetness of life that they are both the same age, and have their birthdays on the same day. They met for the first time on their twenty-first birthdays—and four years later they were married.

And now, if you ask that big successful toffee-man what are the sweetest things in life, he will not say 'Toffees'; he will say the memories and thoughts of those people who love him, and whom he loves.

Things like that never change. As long ago as the time when the Bible was written it was true. If you look up your Bibles, at 2 Samuel 1[23], you will find a wonderful thing said of King Saul and Jonathan: 'Saul and Jonathan were lovely and sweet in their lives.'

That is the kind of sweetness which is most sweet in all the world—sweeter than success, sweeter than toffees.

THE TEACHER WITH INFLUENZA

ONCE there was a lovely teacher called Alice Freeman Palmer. She lived in America, and she was the head of a great college.

But what was really the best thing about her was that she had influenza for years and years.

You musn't think that odd, or start to feel sorry for the teacher, or for the pupils in that great college. It wasn't that kind of influenza—it was a good kind of influenza, not the bad kind that you get in the winter when you've kept your wet shoes on, or played alongside somebody with the sniffles and sneezes. Then, of course, you have to stay indoors, and have lots of handkies and nasty sticky throat lozenges. And if you have it really badly, you have to stay in bed, and have the doctor come to take your temperature and look at your tongue. And when he has gone, you have to shake up the big bottle of medicine he has prescribed, and take it until it's all gone. And there's no getting out of it—because you have influenza, a very nasty thing.

Do you know how that nasty thing got its name? Well, when it first came to England, nobody knew much about it. Except that it was a sickness that one person got from another—it was catching. If a boy or a girl sitting alongside another in a desk at school started sniffing and sneezing, it wasn't very long before the other was sniffing and sneezing too.

And the doctors looked round for a long-sounding name to give that sickness. And they decided on an Italian name—*Influenza*—which really means something that flows out of one life into the lives of others round about.

And it was really a very good name, wasn't it, although the sickness that it stands for is an altogether nasty kind of influenza.

But you see, you can have a good kind, too. That's why I said that that lovely teacher, Alice Freeman Palmer, teacher of that great college, had 'influenza' all her life. She did—she had *influence*, to use our English word for the good kind of influenza. She had a happy face and a happy heart, and she was wise and kind, and the girls loved her.

A long time after she was grown up, one girl wrote: 'When I saw her, I felt as if I could do things that I never dreamed of before. Even now, whenever I think of her, I have a sense of dignity in my life.' (Dignity is a nice true, good feeling.) 'I don't know what it is', she said. 'It seems as if her appreciation of the worth of things puts a spirit into me that carries me along until the next time I think of her. I shouldn't care to go on living in a world where she hadn't been.' Wasn't that a lovely thing to say?

She said she didn't know what it was—but we know what it was, don't we? It was influenza, or *influence*—the good kind—flowing happily out of the life of Alice Freeman Palmer, making others happy and true and glad, too.

For that's one thing about influenza, or influence—the good kind—that it's not easy to have it without others catching it. That's what Paul meant when he wrote in one of his letters that are collected in the back of our New Testaments: 'None of us liveth to himself' (Romans 14[7]). And that's a happy thought; when we smile, other people are likely to catch it from us; when we stop to lend a hand, they are likely to catch the spirit of helpfulness; when we are brave, they are likely to be brave too. Once we're smiling, helpful and brave, we can't help them catching it from us—its just like influenza that puts us into bed, only much, much nicer. It's the good kind—*influence*. And every one of us has it, even the smallest, whether we think about it or not.

THE CLEVER CROWS

EVERYBODY knew old Jonathan, and everybody loved him, the boys and girls especially. His real name was Mr Jonathan Morton—but the boys and girls called him Uncle Jonathan. His heart was full of kindness, and his face was full of smiles—and at the corners of his eyes were little lines spanning out toward his ears, that showed where the smiles had been, called 'crow's feet'.

And for that matter his best story was about crows—real crows, that came to eat up his father's corn. That, of course, was a long time ago—but it was just as real to Uncle Jonathan as if it had happened yesterday, and the boys and girls were never tired of hearing of it.

'Tell us about scaring the crows', they would ask. And old Jonathan would put out his favourite pipe, and lay it away safely in his pocket, and begin. He never varied it, because it was so clear in his mind. It had been his first job—to scare the crows from his father's crops. He wasn't very big, and at first he could only do it on Saturdays, when he hadn't to go to the village school. Little Jonathan liked going to school, but best of all he liked scaring the crows. At first he had a strange kind of rattle, and when he was big enough he had a little gun.

'And what did you do when you had to go to school?' the children always asked. And then he told them about the trick he played on the crows. On school-days, he hoped the crows wouldn't miss him, though there was no sound of a rattle or a gun. But the field was not bare, for all that, and many birds still came. Early on the first school-day of the week, Jonathan took an old broom-stick that had been the handle of the broom with which his mother had brushed out her house, and across it near the top he tied another stick, not quite so long. And on the top of it he placed his old shabby Saturday hat, and on the rest of it he put his old shabby Saturday clothes. Then, when he hoped no birds were looking, he took it out early and stood it up in the field.

It was a good scarecrow—a very good scarecrow indeed —exactly the kind that the poet had in mind when he wrote his little poem describing it:

> 'One shoulder up, the other down,
> His hat upon a broomstick crown;
> I saw', said he, 'a ragged scarecrow stand,
> Guarding the sown and sunlit land.
>
> Awhile I stood, and not a crow
> Near the rich furrows dared to go;
> But when I turned away, why then
> They fell to work like husbandmen.'

And that was exactly what Jonathan's father found. Those old crows were not such duffers after all—indeed, they were very wily and clever. Though the same old Saturday hat and the same old Saturday clothes were in the field, they could tell as easily as easily which was Jonathan and which was the scarecrow. The scarecrow was just a pretence.

Jesus talked about people whose religion was just like that, who hoped that nobody would notice it. But Jesus had noticed it. He said: 'Woe unto you, scribes and Pharisees, hypocrites! for ye devour widow's houses, and for a pretence make long prayer' (Matthew 23[14]). And He told about two men who went into the Temple to pray. One man stood proudly where everybody would see him, and hear him, and used long and fine-sounding words in his prayer. But the other man was so real and sure in his love of God, that he did hardly more than bow his head silently to pray.

Jesus pointed out the difference; one was just scarecrow religion, the other was real.

Our religion—as Paul wrote down in the New Testament—is either '*in pretence or in truth*' (Philippians 1¹⁸). Even a crow can tell the difference.

THE MAN WHO NEVER FORGOT

BRUCE DAHLBERG loved Holland. He loved its windmills holding their proud heads up into the sky, its canals, and its kind Dutch people. But when he thought of Syracuse, not far from New York, his heart was full of longing to get home. Sometimes it seemed as if he would never get home. The enemies of Bruce's country, and of the Dutch, had quickly overrun Holland; many of the people had been killed, and many of the beautiful things broken down.

But did the people of Holland forget to be kind to those who were trying to rid them of their enemies? Oh, no! And they were kind to Bruce, helping him and giving him food.

When at last the happy day of peace came, nobody was more excited about it than Bruce. Now he could rejoice in the freedom of the sun and the air once more. Best of all, he could go back to his own country, and to Syracuse which was his home. His Dutch friends were loth to part with him, but as he waved them good-bye, he called: 'I won't forget you—I won't forget your kindness!'

Months and months went by. At last Bruce found himself home in Syracuse. But not even that excitement caused him to forget. 'I must do something for those kind people', he said. 'I wonder what they would like best.'

After he had puzzled it out for a little while, he said: 'I know what I shall do—I shall do something for the children. They will all like that; for they have all had such a hard time.'

At once Bruce got out his pen and wrote a letter to Holland, to the wife of the burgomaster—the mayor—of the little town where he had received such kindness. 'I want to do something for the children', he wrote. 'If any of your little children need shoes this winter, will you please write down the sizes and the names on a piece of paper?'

And when the wife of the burgomaster read that, she was very glad. How many little children do you think there were in the town who had no shoes? Four hundred! And she very carefully wrote down the name of each of them; then she got each little child to stand on a piece of brown paper while she drew a mark round it with a pencil so that they would get the right sizes. It was a big task; but in the end she posted off the paper and the names to Bruce in Syracuse.

Bruce was waiting for the letter to come, but when it came with four hundred names and sizes he was taken aback. 'Wherever shall I get all these?' he asked himself. 'No preacher's son ever has much money.' And then he thought and thought. 'But I must get them somehow', he said. So he thought of a plan.

He went to the house of a friend near by, and knocked on his door. When his friend opened it, he showed him the letter from Holland, and told him about all the people who had shown him such kindness. 'I must do what I can', he said. 'Perhaps you would like to help.'

And his friend said: 'Yes.' And he gave Bruce money to buy shoes.

Bruce thanked him, and greatly encouraged went to the next door, to the next, and to the next. Always when the people came he told them the same story. And by degrees he made his way from door to door, right through the whole neighbourhood.

All the people who saw his letter and heard his story were so ready to help, that soon Bruce was able to match every little pencil-drawing with a pair of shoes, and tie a name on each, and pack them up in great boxes ready to ship to Holland.

And when at last the great boxes arrived, what a

wonderful day that was. Every little child that winter went shod in a new pair of shoes—sent from right over the sea, by The Man Who Didn't Forget.

In the New Testament that Bruce reads, and that those kind Dutch people read, and that you read, are these words: '*To do good . . . forget not*' (Hebrews 13^{16}).

12

LITTLE ODD TOM

Once, long ago, there lived in Odcombe, in England, an odd little man. His name was Tom—Tom Coryate. He called himself 'The Odcombe Legge Stretcher'. He had a merry heart and a quick tongue, and he was a great traveller.

Men and women might go about the land in their great lumbering coaches, but Tom liked to walk.

He shod himself in a good pair of shoes, slung a bag over his shoulder, and set off. At the end of every road he felt some adventure awaited him. And he certainly did have a great many—between sleeping like a beggar in the ditch and like a prince in the King's court.

Everywhere he went people enjoyed his stories and his witty replies. And when he had stretched his legs in England, he made up his mind to go farther, and to see other countries. He went to France, travelling with little more than the pair of shoes on his feet and the shirt on his back. From France he went to Italy, and from Italy to Switzerland, from Switzerland to Germany. And all the way he laughed with the people, and made friends. In Germany, near a dark forest one night, he was surprised by some robbers. For a moment he wondered what to do. But his quick wit saved him. Without waiting for them to set upon him and take his money, he took off his hat, and bowing lowly began to beg in a pitiful voice. And the robbers really thought he *was* a beggar, and instead of knocking him down for money they tossed him a few coins from their own money-bags.

When at last little odd Tom got back to Odcombe, he had had so many adventures that he wrote a book about them—and that was the very first travel-book in our

English language. He gave it a funny title: *Coryates Crudities, hastily gobled up in five months travells*.

Soon, little odd Tom was itching to be off again. This time, on leaving Odcombe, he addressed a farewell message to his friends at the village-cross. Then he stepped into the church to pray for God's blessing on his journey, and to take off his worn shoes and hang them up in the church as a sign of his thanksgiving for the ways he had been and the adventures he had enjoyed. (Little did he know that the people would keep them hanging up there for a hundred years. But they did.)

Little odd Tom got as far as the beautiful and ancient cities of Greece; he went to Constantinople, to Cairo, and to Jerusalem. When he came home he brought, among other things, the first table-forks seen in England. But most of all, people came to treasure his travel-book that told them of strange lands and peoples.

Nowadays there are lots of travel-books, and some of them are specially for boys and girls. They tell us about strange lands, and of beautiful and interesting things. But chiefly they tell us about the people. And that is best of all. For whatever people are like, and wherever they live, they are God's children, and only as we get to know them and love them, can we have a happy and peaceful world together.

> *Remember all the people*
> *Who live in far-off lands*
> *In strange and lovely cities,*
> *Or roam the desert sands,*
> *Or farm the mountain pastures,*
> *Or till the endless plains*
> *Where children wade through rice-fields,*
> *And watch the camel-trains.*
>
> *Some work in sultry forests*
> *Where apes swing to and fro,*
> *Some fish in mighty rivers,*
> *Some hunt across the snow.*

Remember all God's children,
Who yet have never heard
The truth that comes from Jesus,
The glory of His Word.

PERCY DEARMER

13

COCKY ROBERTS

LITTLE Ignace Paderewski clambered up on to the piano stool, but his feet couldn't reach the floor. He was only three, but he liked to play. When he was seven, he was playing beautifully, and composing—making and writing his own music—and by the time he was grown up he was famous as one of the great pianists of his day.

People who loved beautiful music gathered to hear him, and soon his fame spread far beyond Poland. From country to country he made his way, and everywhere people gathered to listen to him. He made many friends.

But his most surprising friend was Cocky Roberts.

Paderewski was feeling a little gloomy the day they met. He had had to miss his first concert in Melbourne because he had hurt his finger. He couldn't even go out walking in the streets and the parks of the city because of the rain. The sky was gloomy grey, and Paderewski was gloomy too.

But Cocky Roberts soon changed all that. He was a happy, friendly, talkative parrot. And after that winter's day they were never parted.

From country to country they made their way together, Paderewski and Cocky Roberts. Only when the seas were rough did Cocky Roberts find it hard to keep up his chatter. But once ashore, he was as lively as ever.

Often when his master had practice to do, he would slip away and close the door of the music-room. But soon there would be a little knock at the door. Sometimes, for fun, Paderewski would pretend not to hear. But it was no use. In a little time a second knock would come from a strong beak. Still in fun, Paderewski would call out: 'Who is there?'

Then a little voice would say clearly: 'Cocky Roberts!'

'Who?' his master would say, still pretending.

Again the answer would come, this time a little louder, 'Cocky Roberts! Cocky Roberts!'

So Paderewski would have to rise and let him in.

No sooner was he in than he would walk over and perch on his master's foot whilst he practised. And though he had sometimes to use the pedal of the piano very hard, it did not in the least disturb Cocky Roberts. For hours he would sit perfectly still, whilst his master went through his music. And then, of a sudden, he would break his silence by saying something that, from a parrot, was surprising: '*Oh Lord, how beautiful! How beautiful!*'

It sounded a very surprising thing from a Cocky, even though Cocky Roberts was a surprising Cocky. Of course, human beings—men and women and boys and girls—can't help but rejoice in the beautiful things God has made for us.

And there are times when we can hardly help singing our hymn:

For the beauty of the earth,
  For the beauty of the skies,
For the love which from our birth
  Over and around us lies,

Gracious God, to Thee we raise
This our sacrifice of praise.

14

THE SELFISH EMPRESS

In the beautiful sunny land of Mexico once lived a clever gardener. He loved his garden, and he tended it so wisely that whatever he put in it grew.

One year there appeared in his garden some flowers that nobody had ever seen before. And when he first saw them he was very excited. They were large and beautiful and full of the sun. And one of the strange things about them was that they grew from dull, dry-looking roots that seemed as though they could never produce anything beautiful.

As he tended his beautiful Botanic Garden in Mexico City he fell to thinking of a friend who was a gardener— in charge of the Royal Gardens at Madrid in Spain. 'I must send him a present of some of my new flowers', he said. 'At least, I must send him some of the roots, so that he can grow these beautiful flowers, too, in the sunny land of Spain.' And he did.

When his friend received them, he was astonished to find that they hadn't a name. At once he set about finding them one, and by the time they had come into flower in his garden he had succeeded. He called them after one of the famous botanists of the day, Dr Andreas Dahl—and ever since they have been called dahlias.

Dr Dahl was carried away with joy to learn that the new flowers had been called after him. As well as the flowers, he thought that something might be made of the roots. 'Perhaps', he said, 'if people only get to know them and like them, they might dig them up sometimes and eat them instead of potatoes. They might prove a nice change.' But although a few people tried cooking their dahlia roots for dinner, they didn't like them.

But they soon became popular flowers. One of the first to grow dahlias was a queen—the Empress Josephine. She lived in France, and at a place called the Malmaison she had a beautiful garden. Soon, the dahlias that she grew were the best in the world. When the flowering time came she invited her friends to come and see them. One of those invited was a princess, Princess Marie Louise.

As soon as the Princess saw the beautiful dahlia flowers, she made up her mind to have some too. But the Empress Josephine was very selfish with her flowers. She wanted to keep them all to herself. She wanted her garden to be famous for having the best collection of dahlias in the world.

But the time came when she had to have the help of a gardener—they had grown to be so many—and that was the undoing of the selfish Empress. One of her ladies-in-waiting had never forgotten how the Empress had refused a root to the Princess. And she made up her mind that she would defeat her selfishness. Her lover was a young prince, and she got him to go in secret to the Empress's gardener and ask for dahlia roots. The gardener gave him some, and in time they were planted in Paris, where they came into flower and were beautiful.

All was well, until someone carried news of what had happened to the Empress Josephine. When she heard how her selfish plan had been defeated, she flew into a rage. And at once she dismissed the gardener, and sent away from her court the young lady-in-waiting and her lover. And what was more silly, she gave up all interest in dahlias for ever.

Empress though she was, she had not learned the secret of a true gardener. And it is one of the happiest secrets in the whole world. Jesus said so. He said: 'Freely ye have received, freely give' (Matthew 10⁸).

15

BEGINNING AT BETHLEHEM

THE boys and girls all loved to play with little Phillips Brooks. No one ever caught him down in the dumps. 'Anyone can tell when Phillips is around', they said, 'because he is always singing.' And he was. By the time he was twelve, he knew the words and the tunes of two hundred hymns off by heart, as well as lots of songs.

And when he was grown up, and had become the minister of Holy Trinity Church in Philadelphia, he had lovely singing in his church.

One day the people of that great church let out a secret. 'It is time', they said, 'that our minister had a long holiday.' And they collected enough to send him away to the Holy Land where Jesus had lived—to walk its streets, and to look at its wild flowers and birds and skies.

It was a wonderful secret, and a wonderful holiday. When Christmas Eve came, Phillips Brooks was able to go out from Jerusalem to the little town of Bethlehem. It was a beautiful night, calm and still. And as he stood listening to the men and women and little children singing their praises to God for the gift of Jesus on the first Christmas Eve, *his* heart welled over with praises, too. So it came about that a little while later he sat down and wrote one of the loveliest Christmas hymns in the whole world.

> *O little town of Bethlehem,*
> *How still we see thee lie!*
> *Above thy deep and dreamless sleep*
> *The silent stars go by:*
> *Yet in thy dark street shineth*
> *The everlasting Light;*
> *The hopes and fears of all the years*
> *Are met in thee tonight.*

D

How silently, how silently
  The wondrous gift is given!
So God imparts to human hearts
  The blessings of His heaven.
No ear can hear His coming;
  But in this world of sin,
Where meek souls will receive Him, still
  The dear Christ enters in.

All his happy life long—from the time Phillips Brooks was a boy singing at his play to when he was a famous preacher—Jesus, who had come into the world in Bethlehem, was his best Friend. And when at last he died, and those who loved him in Philadelphia and Boston wished to put up a statue of him, they engaged the cleverest sculptor in the land.

With his specially chosen block of stone, and his chisels, and memory, he set to work. But he could not get his work to come right. When he wanted to make it look happy, it failed to look strong, and when he made it look strong, it failed to look friendly. So he broke it all up with his big hammer, and started again. And still it would not come right—and he broke it up again—and again and again, five times, till he was almost in despair.

Then he took a fine piece of his best stone and made a figure of Jesus. And only when it was finished, and set there, did he fashion the figure of Phillips Brooks. And in his sculpture he placed the hand of Jesus on the shoulder of Phillips Brooks, and he turned the face of the beloved preacher toward Jesus. At last he was satisfied with his work—and everybody else was, too. For they said, when they saw the beautiful sculpture: 'That's how it was! Jesus was always first with Phillips Brooks and His hand, it seemed, was always on his shoulder, helping him, making him happy and glad and good.'

And that, of course, was why everybody loved him.

16

HOW COURAGE CAME TO THE PEOPLE

How many cities have you been in? Count up!

Sometimes we sing a children's hymn about cities. It begins:

> *Remember all the people*
> *Who live in far-off lands*
> *In strange and lovely cities,*
> *Or roam the desert sands.*

One of the world's 'strange and lovely cities' is Warsaw. It stands right in the middle of Poland, on the banks of a great river. And a great many people live there: a great many boys and girls. For hundreds of years boats have gone up and down the river, and for hundreds of years people have built their red-roofed houses on its banks, among the trees. Some seemed very old, some very beautiful. They belonged to the one-time rich merchant princes; and long after they ceased to live in them, the old houses still kept their special names and coats-of-arms— they were so special. One was called The House of the Ships, another The House of the Lions, another The House of the Negro. You may be sure that thrilling stories lay behind those special names of the princes' houses. Some of them had beautiful doors, wrought in iron and bronze and wood. And all the boys and girls who lived in Warsaw loved them.

As well as the river rolling along, and the beautiful old houses, there were many narrow streets in the city, where the sunbeams danced and made pretty patterns. And under some of them were secret passages. Nobody knew quite where they all led, only that down below there were good hiding-places. And lots of times, through the centuries, when the enemies of the city came, the people went down there.

Besides, in the 'strange and lovely' city there were the castle, and the cathedral. And there were many churches, with their spires reaching high up into the sky, with doors for the people to go in, and bells to ring out over the city for very gladness. And there were shops and schools and parks, and stretching from side to side of the river, fine bridges.

But I must tell you that it isn't like that any more—no, it isn't a 'strange and lovely' city any more.

Not very long ago, sad to say, enemy aircraft came with bombs and guns, and broke it all down. In olden times, the people could easily have been warned by the soldiers at the castle, and have run into their hiding-places. But it wasn't like that.

And soon parts of the city were all broken into ruins. Soon it must have seemed to the people who lived there, and to the boys and girls especially, that *everything* they valued was gone.

Then suddenly they knew that it wasn't so. For as they passed along the street by the depôt—a kind of shop—of the British and Foreign Bible Society, where they sold Bibles and New Testaments, they saw that where the windows had been blown out, there remained in one a little piece of shattered glass. It had been part of a beautiful window, with words on it—and now it was all that was left. And when the people passed, they paused, and some took off their hats, and some bowed their heads, and all took courage. For those words were the words of Jesus; and they said something that seemed specially wonderful just then: '*Heaven and earth shall pass away, but My words shall not pass away*' (Matthew 24^{35}). Though the people of Warsaw were sad to have lost so much of their 'strange and lovely city', they were glad to have still the wonderful words of Jesus—words of love and truth and care.

17

LITTLE SILVER BELLS

LET me tell you the story of the little silver bells.

You know what a synagogue is? It's a Jewish church—very different from ours, but the kind of church Jesus went to when He was a boy.

I don't suppose you have ever been inside a synagogue. It is a very sacred place to Jewish boys and girls, just as our church is to us. And lots of boys and girls still go to it—not only in Palestine, but in our own land. It is in many ways very different from our church.

One of the great differences is that the people who go to the synagogue have no Bible, such as we have, set up for the minister to read. They have instead what they call the *Torah*—the first five books of the Bible, the Law of Moses.

It doesn't look a bit like our Bible—a book with pages, and a nice strong cover. It is a scroll, and looks something like a small map that might have come from a school-wall. Only, of course, it's much smaller, and much more precious, and is kept carefully rolled when it is not being read. It is written on parchment, and on the ends of each of the rollers there are—what do you think?—little silver bells!

They are lovely little bells, and their being there is something really special.

I wish we had bells like them on our Bible in church. In the synagogue, whenever the *Torah*, the scroll of the Law, is taken up and read, the little silver bells tinkle. And the girls and boys love that, not to mention the big people. And when they understand what it means they love it even more. The little silver bells, tinkling when the Law is read, are a sign of the joy of the people as they listen to it.

And one day each year a special festival is held, called the 'Rejoicing of the Law'. On that day in synagogues all over the world, the Law is not only read, it is carried in a procession of rejoicing seven times round the synagogue, to the tinkling of the little bells.

You can imagine how the girls and boys like that festival, especially when they have a part in it. From olden times they have been allowed to join in the procession after their elders, and carry little scrolls of their own, and little paper flags. At the end of the procession everyone joins hands in a big circle, and dancing, sings: 'Let us rejoice and be glad with this Law, for it is strength and light for us!'

Now you see why I wish we had little bells attached to our Bible in church. It would be lovely to hear them when the minister reads to us from its pages. But we don't do things that way, although we do have a day that is a kind of festival. We call it 'Bible Sunday', and it comes every year on the same day. And though we don't have little bells, we ought to rejoice on that day even more than the Jewish girls and boys—because we have so much more to rejoice in. They have the sacred Law of the Old Testament, but we have the New Testament, too. And that is a great deal more precious, because it tells us all the stories of Jesus; of His coming as a tiny babe, of His love that took Him to the Cross, and of His victory over death so that now He lives for evermore. We ought to rejoice when we hear our Bible read.

And in it—just like a little silver bell—there is a text to remind us. It says: '*Rejoice in the Lord alway: and again I say, Rejoice!*' (Philippians 4[4]).

18

TIMOTHY'S DREAM

Visiting a big store is great fun, isn't it? I liked visiting Timothy Eaton's store. It is a wonderful store; the largest in Canada. And there's a wonderful story behind it.

Timothy grew up in Ireland. His home was poor, and his widowed mother had a struggle to get enough for her nine children to eat. So when he was thirteen, Timothy went to work. He found work with a merchant. It was hard work, starting early in the morning, and continuing long after most boys and girls were in bed. Sometimes it was midnight before Timothy was able to crawl into his own little bed under the counter.

By the end of five years Timothy made up his mind that he would change lots of things if ever he had a store of his own. But he was only a youth, and he had to wait a long time for his dream to come true.

Because things were so hard in Ireland, some of his brothers and sisters said good-bye, and went off to Canada. And after a while they persuaded Timothy to join them.

The great new country was very different from Ireland, but Timothy soon found work. He started in one store, and then moved to another. At last—and he was thirty-five before the chance came—he bought a little one of his own in Toronto.

In those days shopping was very different; there were few fixed prices. It was the custom of shopkeepers to put much bigger prices on their goods than they really hoped to get, much bigger prices than they knew the things were worth. If the customers were silly enough to pay them, then the shopkeepers were well pleased. But if they set out to argue that the prices were too high, then they might be brought down a little. And sometimes the arguments went on right into the night, for the shops were often still selling at midnight.

Timothy Eaton was quite sure that this was all wrong. The prices were too high, the shops kept open too long, and no one really knew by the price-tickets what a thing was to cost.

So he set about to work out his dream—a different kind of store. And he put an advertisement in the paper to say that he proposed to sell goods cheaper—that he was going to sell them for cash only, not in exchange for goods, as some of the other stores did, and that the prices would be exactly what the price-tickets said. His store would open just like the others, at eight o'clock in the morning, but it would close at six; and if anybody was dissatisfied with anything, they were to bring it back. It was all so straightforward and fair, that it was Timothy's boast that even a child could shop in his store.

It was only a very little store, with oil-lamps, and in the winter a little square stove. But it was quite different from any of the other stores. It was a fair and friendly place.

And it prospered. As the town grew bigger, Timothy made his store bigger. And today it is so big that more than 13,000 people work in it in Toronto—and there are lots of branches in other parts of Canada.

When Timothy—grown old, making his store the right kind of store—died in 1907, one of Canada's big newspapers said this: 'Mr Eaton has shown that a successful business-man can be good, clean, one might say holy. His was a beautiful life, and he will long be mourned and never be forgotten.'

Wasn't that a wonderful thing to say?

And those who shop in his big store today, and those who worship in the Timothy Eaton Memorial Church, don't forget him.

19

THE LAND OF THE LITTLE WOVEN BASKET

LOTS of people knew Mrs Ropes. She lived in a pleasant house in Brookline, in a part of America called Massachusetts. Her husband loved ships—fine sailing clipper-ships, that sailed away to strange, interesting ports. And although they were the fastest ships afloat, often he was gone for months, to get precious cargoes of silks and tea and rice.

One time when he was away, Mrs Ropes thought she would have a party. First, she sat down and made a list of all the people she wanted to come. Then she thought of something nice to eat; and because it was to be a very special party, she talked it over with her cook, and her little housemaid.

And soon the whole house was in a pleasant bustle. The cook got out her cooking-board, her flour-sifter and rolling-pin, and made the very nicest little cakes you ever did see, and put them in little tins, and set a cherry on the top of each. Then she rolled out some pastry, and made little tarts.

The little housemaid got out her polishing-cloth, and polished up the furniture, and mopped the floor till it shone. Then she dusted all the pictures and the things on the mantel-shelf, and raced into the garden to pick fresh flowers for the vases.

And the day came. The calendar on the wall said the year was 1827. But everybody knew that, and nobody took special notice—not then. It was far more important that the day was fine and sunny, with a ripple of excitement in the hearts of Mrs Ropes, the cook, the little serving-maid, and in the hearts of everybody coming to the party.

At last when they were all ready in their best dresses,

there came the first knock at the door. And soon there was another knock, and another and another. In no time all the friends invited were seated in the pleasant sitting-room, with the floor shining, and the furniture all beautifully dusted, and fresh flowers in the vases.

No sooner had the excited guests seated themselves, than one of them exclaimed at the sight of a little woven basket on a table. It was a beautiful little basket, and different from anything she had ever seen before. 'What a beautiful little basket that is, Mrs Ropes', said she. 'Wherever did it come from?'

'Japan', Mrs Ropes answered eagerly. 'My husband brought it home in one of his clipper-ships.'

'Wherever is Japan?' all the ladies asked at once.

Mrs Ropes explained that nobody knew much about Japan, because Japan was a kind of hermit country living shut up all to itself. Great painted signs at the ports warned foreigners to keep away, saying that if the King of Spain, or even the Christian's God Himself should try to enter, they would be beheaded.

The ladies at the party were shocked to hear that. 'What dreadfully unhappy people they must be', they said, 'if they don't know that God is not a robber waiting to break into their country, but a God of love.' And then they made a suggestion. 'It seems we should pray for Japan, and all the people in that little unhappy country.'

And they did.

By the time they had finished praying, and had come to the tea and the little cakes and tarts, somebody said: 'I think we should start to save money enough to send Bibles to that little unhappy country.' And they did. And before long, they had gathered together six hundred dollars, which is a very big sum of money.

But there was just one obstacle—they were not allowed to send Bibles to Japan. So what did they do? Well, they put the money in the Bank, and kept on saving more, because they thought it wasn't just enough to pray for the land of the little woven basket. And by the time the money had grown seven times as large, the obstacles were removed, and they were able to share what they knew of the loving goodness and greatness of God, with the people of Japan.

No wonder Mrs Ropes always said that that was the best party she ever had—because it reached all the way from Brookline to the land of the little woven basket.

20

MR ANONYMOUS

JILL and Sue were the best of friends. And they spent all their holidays together. They were good at making up games. One of their best for bedtime was played when the light was out.

'Your turn', Sue would say. And Jill would begin to rattle off the names she knew, beginning with a given letter of the alphabet. 'J for Jill—that was easy: J for Jean, J for Joan, J for John.'

Then it was Sue's turn: 'K for Kath . . .' And then her own again: 'L for Laurie'—there were lots. Some letters were as easy as easy, some were hard. Then she was tempted to make up one. But that wasn't fair. Soon they were rattling through to the end: X was hard, Y was hard, and Z wasn't any better.

Then it was Sue's turn, to start the alphabet all over again. She was lucky—they both knew lots for A. But one night Sue began by popping in a new one: 'A for Anonymous.'

'You can't have that', said Jill, 'that isn't a name.'

'Yes, it is', said Sue, 'I saw it once when I was on holiday with Daddy. It was in a place in the city of Budapest, shaded by some beautiful trees. It was on a monument.'

'I've never heard of him', said Jill, 'who was he?'

'I don't know *everything* about him', answered Sue. 'I asked Daddy, and he said his real name is Mr Nobody.'

'There!' said Jill, 'I told you!'

'Well', Sue went on, 'his monument is up in an important place in Budapest, and that shows he's important. Daddy said that long ago, when the people thought of the unknown man who patiently collected up all the stories of their brave and adventurous past, when they first made a little kingdom for themselves in Hungary, and built their lovely city on the banks of the river Danube, they felt they never wanted to forget him. So they engaged clever craftsmen, and they worked with all their skill, and made this monument of Anonymous. And they put it up in a good place, where the people passed to and fro all the day, so that they could never forget him.'

'Is he still there?' asked Jill.

'Yes, he's still there', said Sue, 'sitting with his great roll of paper by his side—parchment, Daddy called it. And he's nice—his head is bent just as if he is thinking of the adventurous days of the past, and he has his pen in his hand. He has a long cloak on, and a cowl over his head— and you can just see his toes peeping out from under his cloak. But you can't see his face—for his cowl, and the sunshine and shadow of the beautiful trees. But Daddy said that didn't matter, because all his life long Anonymous wanted always to help—but he never wanted to be *praised* for helping.'

'Yes,' said Jill, 'I suppose that is wonderful, when you think of it—to want to help all your life, and not want to be praised for helping.'

Said Sue: 'I'd like to be called Miss Anonymous, wouldn't you?'

Jill thought for a whole long minute.

Then forgetting all about finishing their game, they both snuggled down.

But they remembered about Miss Anonymous again next day, when the sun was up.

21

TOP OF THE WORLD

NOT everyone can buy honey from a giant—not outside fairy-stories. But we can in Auckland. For Sir Edmund Hillary lives here, and works on his bee-farm. Here, a smiling giant, six foot two, he walks about in the sweet sun and air, with dreams of the mountains in his heart.

He was a schoolboy when he first went climbing. A master took Ed. Hillary and his friends to the mountains. All his holidays after that were spent in the mountains. He saved his pocket-money to get the best guide, and he did everything he could to keep fit.

He hoped some day to be good enough to climb a really great mountain—and that day came. He was chosen by Sir John Hunt to be one of his men to climb Everest, the greatest mountain in the world.

It took a long time just to get ready. Hundreds of people helped. Special tents had to be made, and special boots; oxygen-sets had to be tested for breathing up where the air was thin; and special ropes had to be got; and clothes designed to be light and warm and waterproof. And there were stores—enough for many men for many months. And it all took a long time, and a great deal of hard work and patience.

At long last, as they drew near, a line of strong brown-faced men of the mountains had to be got to help with the loads. Everything had to be carried—higher and higher.

And a time came when they all had to be left behind. Only five picked men managed to struggle to Camp Nine. And soon three of those had to go back.

That left only two brave, strong men—Hillary and his Sherpa friend Tensing. High on the mountain, in their little tent that shivered in the wind, they spent the night. They couldn't sleep; and at four in the morning Hillary looked out. It was very dark, and his boots were frozen stiff. But soon he was able to heat them over the primus stove, and make ready a little food and warm drinks. And by the time the sun was up, Hillary and Tensing were off, kicking and hacking out hard icy steps.

How high they were, and what hard work it was! Would they never get there? The last part of the climb was along a 'knife-edge ridge' of rock and ice and snow. The air was so thin, that without their oxygen-sets they couldn't have lived, let alone climbed. But they pressed on, higher and higher.

Telling of it at last when he came home, Hillary said: 'I had been cutting steps continuously for two hours, and Tensing, too, was moving very slowly. As I chipped steps around still another corner, I wondered rather dully just how long we could keep it up. . . . I looked upward to see a narrow snow ridge running up to a snowy peak.' And then he said a really thrilling thing: 'A few more whacks of the ice-axe in the firm snow, and *we stood on the top!*'

That's how they did it!

But suppose Hillary hadn't been able to make those 'few more whacks'. Suppose they hadn't been able to scramble up that last *two feet*—for Everest is twenty-nine thousand and *two feet!* They wouldn't have conquered the greatest mountain in the world. But they did, because they 'endured unto the end'.

And that's a thrilling secret—for boys and girls who want to get a hard thing done, as well as for mountaineers —to 'endure unto the end' (Mark 13¹³).

22

SWEETHEART ABBEY

IN Scotland, near Dumfries, is a memorial abbey—a kind of church—called Sweetheart Abbey. Isn't that a nice name?

It was built by a lady a long, long time ago as a memorial to her husband, who was her sweetheart all his life. She was a very beautiful lady called Devorgilla.

And today, anyone who goes to Sweetheart Abbey can see what remains of it, built in rosy red stone, and partly covered with creeper. All around its square tower is soft green grass.

The sad part is that all memorials crumble. The rains and the sun and the winds beat down upon them, and they crumble.

But happily there is another kind of memorial—only one—that never crumbles. No matter what rains and sun and winds beat down upon it, it never crumbles. It is the memorial of deeds.

Once in a house where Jesus was having His meal with some friends, reclining at table, a woman came with a very precious and fragrant gift. It was something she valued very much, but not too much to give it to Jesus. And as He reclined at table, resting His feet on the couch —as people did in those days—she came in very quietly and broke the precious box of ointment over His feet. It refreshed His feet, and made the whole house smell fragrant. And though she didn't say anything about it, in a very little time everybody in the house knew what had happened. Of course it was a lovely thing to do, and you can't keep a lovely thing to yourself. But one of the disciples thought it was a waste. 'Why, it was precious,' he said, 'it could have been sold and given to the poor.'

But Jesus didn't think of it that way at all. He knew why the woman had poured out her precious gift so generously. And He said a very beautiful thing about it, which is written in our Bible: 'I tell you,' He said, 'wheresoever this Gospel shall be preached through the whole world, this also that she hath done shall be spoken of for a memorial of her.'

That is the only kind of memorial that lasts—the memorial of great and loving deeds.

The rosy stone of Sweetheart Abbey in Scotland is crumbling now, after six hundred years, but happily, the sweetheart whom it recalls, has this other and better kind of memorial, too. Before he died, for thirty-five happy years, he and his wife Devorgilla lived together, and did many good deeds. They built churches for the people. They built a lovely bridge over the river at Dumfries and it still stands. They founded Balliol College, at Oxford, one of the loveliest and most famous colleges— and young people can still go there to learn.

So neither the Lady Devorgilla, nor her husband, will ever be forgotten now—because, they too have filled the world with fragrant deeds.

23

TWO EYES, THREE EYES

THE wind raced along the streets of the city by the sea, telling its secrets to those who would listen. But few people, as they climbed Wellington's hilly streets, stopped to listen. They were too busy, which was a pity, for up at the University that day something of great importance had happened. Two little sleepy, friendly lizards had been hatched—two little Tua-taras. They were important —not just because Tua-taras, who live in New Zealand, are the only three-eyed creatures in the world, but also because these little Tua-taras were the first ever to be hatched in captivity.

So no wonder Mr Dawbin at the University was excited. He loved Tua-tara lizards, and understood them, but he had never had two baby ones to tend before; nobody had.

He carefully prepared a safe place for them, the kind of place he knew they would like; he fed them with the kind of food that he knew they would like, and day after day he watched over them very carefully. He marked down in his note-book when they were three-inches long, and the joyous news, at the end of a fortnight, that they seemed to be growing well. And he was proud of them, and had their photographs put in the newspaper.

Soon lots of boys and girls came knocking, asking if they could see the little Tua-taras. And they were such friendly little fellows, that the boys and girls chatted about them for days.

'How would you like to have three eyes, instead of two', asked Tommy Lee—'one on each side, and one in the middle?'

Betty, his sister, answered at once, 'I think it would be

good—then I might be able to see what I do now, and half as much again.'

'But I don't think it would work out like that at all', said Dick. 'In any case, God has given us two eyes—not three—and sometimes it must seem to Him that we don't use those two very well.'

And I think Dick was right.

Have you ever noticed six words in the New Testament: 'As Jesus passed by He saw . . .' What did He see? Well, everything that was about Him—the birds and the skies and the flowers. But often, as those words in the New Testament tell, He saw things that nobody else saw.

One day, 'As He passed by, He saw Levi the son of Alphæus sitting at the receipt of custom . . .' (Mark 2¹⁴). And He saw that he was unhappy. He didn't like his work, for it was hateful work, taking from the people high taxes, much more than was fair and just. And so Jesus called him to follow Him, and to bring his pen and his skill and use it for something better. And he did.

Another day—and it is recorded in the same chapter (Mark 2⁵)—four men came along carrying a sick friend on his mattress. And 'when Jesus saw their faith, He said unto the sick of the palsy, Son, thy sins be forgiven thee'. And He made him better straight away.

Often and often Jesus did things like that—using His eyes to see what nobody else saw.

If only we could use our eyes as Jesus did, how wonderful it would be; for two eyes are quite enough if only we use them well and have love in them.

24

FOLLOW MY LEADER

Isn't it fun to play 'Follow My Leader'? If you have a brave and daring leader, he can jump ditches, climb banks, and run over rough ground, and take you into all sorts of hard places. And always you have to follow. If you fail to follow, you have to fall out and go to the very end of the row, and that is a kind of disgrace.

And it's great fun to play 'Follow My Leader', as you grow up, though you don't play it in quite the same way.

Young Lieutenant Rawson played 'Follow My Leader' with the British Army. It was in Egypt. A rebellion had broken out, and General Wolseley and his British men had been sent to deal with it.

Unlike the rebel leader, General Wolseley didn't know the country very well, and what he had to do wasn't a bit easy. But he set about his plans as best he could. He seized the famous Canal—the Suez Canal—so that the rebels couldn't use it, and he landed his men safely.

And so secretly and successfully was his plan carried out, that after a short, sharp encounter, the rebels were completely defeated.

But how did he find his way into strange Tel-el-Kebir, to defeat the rebels? Ah, that's the secret! He didn't know the way himself. He was led by young Lieutenant Rawson. General Wolseley and his men just played 'Follow My Leader'.

Lieutenant Rawson was very young, but he proved a fine leader. His only compass was the stars, but on and on he went, until the job was done. Sadly, he was among the first to be wounded when the clash came with the rebels. When that was known, and how badly he was wounded, General Wolseley came instantly.

'I want to ask you one question, sir', he said.

'Yes', said General Wolseley, 'what is it?'

And the young leader asked his question, his eyes out-shining the eagerness of his heart. *'Didn't I lead you straight, General?'*

And when the answer came, *'Yes, you did'*, a smile of contentment broke over his face.

Didn't I lead you straight? It still keeps on happening, this story, for people are still following leaders—good ones and bad ones. Young Lieutenant Rawson was a good leader; he led them straight.

What kind of a leader are you? 'Oh,' you say, 'I'm not a leader.'

But you are. Everyone of us is a leader for someone else to follow. What you say and do matter. There is always someone else following—a little brother, a class-mate, or a playfellow. You mightn't even know. But be a good leader—lead him straight!

The way to be a good leader is to follow some greater Leader yourself. That's what Peter and James and John found long ago—and it's still the most important thing in the world. Jesus, the good, strong, brave Leader of good, brave, strong men came down the beach one day where they were mending their nets, and called, 'Follow Me!' And they followed Him. Life was never dull after that.

And it's not a day too late for you and me to join in. Read your New Testament to find out what sort of a Leader He is, and what He wants you to do, and His call will come to you. You know what those two ringing words mean? 'Follow Me!' They mean Think the way I think, Be brave, Be true, Lend a hand, Love God—and never give up!

He is the grandest Leader of all!

25

WHAT HAPPENED TO THE PEOPLE OF ONO

TRAVELLERS into strange places are often surprised at what they find; Paul was when he found in Athens an altar 'To The Unknown God', and Josiah was at what he found in Ono, Fiji.

A great sickness spread among the people of Ono, until ever so many of them were sick. And they were so sick, that many of them died, and all of them were filled with fear. They tried everything they could think of to rid themselves of the sickness, but no prayers or offerings to the ancient gods were any good.

Just then a canoe came to their little islands. In Tonga the man in the canoe had heard of the missionaries. 'Perhaps', said he, 'you ought to pray to the God of the missionaries. They say that He is the God of the whole world.'

'But we cannot pray to Him', said the sick people. 'Only one man here can pray, and he is the priest of the old religion. We do not know how to pray.'

Days passed, and when the sickness showed no signs of ending, the people, in desperation, came to the priest. At first he refused, but as they continued to beg his help he finally agreed to pray for them to the God he himself did not know. 'Lord, Jehovah,' he prayed, 'here are Thy people. They would worship Thee. I turn my back on Thee for the present, and am on another tack, worshipping another god. But do Thou bless Thy people, and keep them from harm, and do them good.'

Not once but many times he prayed the same prayer. And soon, to everyone's joy, the sickness began to pass away. So the faith of the people of Ono in their old gods was shaken, and they began to turn to the God of the missionaries.

Then Josiah arrived. His canoe had been blown out of its course. He was a Christian, and when he heard what had been happening to the people of Ono, he offered to stay awhile and teach them all *he* knew. He taught them the Lord's Prayer, and some of the story of the life and death of Jesus, and of His rising again. And the people built a little church, and kept the first day of the week as a day of rest and worship.

Gradually, news of the people of Ono got out to the big world. And one of the first things their white Christian friends did was to send them a trained teacher, who knew much more than Josiah knew. And when the first white missionaries themselves were able to visit Ono, they found, to their great joy, nearly all the people worshipping God and living good and happy lives. And among them was the old heathen priest, who at the start had only been able to pray to the unknown God.

Long, long ago now, missionaries came to *our* land. So we don't have to pray to the unknown God—we know what God is like. Jesus has told us. He said . . . 'he that hath seen Me hath seen the Father' (John 14⁹).

Aren't we fortunate?

26

THE MAN WHO STOOD UP TO THINGS

IT was a very special day. Nobody—the King, the Queen, Mrs Roosevelt, the crowd, or the small boy in the crowd —would ever forget it.

They had gathered in London to watch Mrs Roosevelt unveil a fine memorial statue of her late husband, the President of the United States. But when they looked at that fine statue of the President standing there in grey-green bronze, they couldn't help wondering why it had been made like that. For the President had suffered a cruel paralysis of his legs, and for many years had not been able to stand at all. Most of his work—travelling, meeting people, making speeches—had had to be done sitting. That's why they couldn't help wondering why his statue had been made to show him standing up.

But on the edge of the crowd in Grosvenor Square that day was a small boy. And when he heard the people talking, he said: 'I guess I know why.'

He had been remembering the story of the President— long before he *was* President—out with his family on a holiday, teaching his boys to sail a boat. Suddenly they had spied a forest fire, and at once Mr Roosevelt, had turned the boat for the shore, to help. Putting out the fire proved dangerous and dirty work, and they got very hot and tired. When the excitement was over, the boys' father had suggested a swim. The boys had enjoyed that, and so had their father; and when they got back to where they were staying, he went for another. Later, when he ran home, the mail had just come, and Mr Roosevelt sat down in his wet bathing-suit to read the letters.

Suddenly, he felt chilly, and then his legs felt funny.

When the doctor came he had to tell Mr Roosevelt that

he was paralysed. Try as he would, he couldn't stand. He had to take to crutches.

For three long years he battled on. Then news reached him of a young man who had been completely cured by exercising his legs in the pool at Warm Springs. Soon Mr Roosevelt was there too—patiently, patiently exercising under water. For a long time he kept it up, and soon he was feeling a little better. One day some newspapermen came to see him to write up his story in the newspaper. Lots of people read it, and soon, from all over the land, men and women and boys and girls who were crippled were making their way to Warm Springs.

But there wasn't room for them all to stay. So the big, smiling Mr Roosevelt set about thinking out a plan. First he sought out a good doctor, and together they worked out a list of exercises; then he got some old cottages cleaned and made comfortable for the crippled people to stay in. Next he bought the Warm Springs, for a very great sum of money. He wanted to make sure that the people who came would never be turned away. His friends helped him, and more and more people came.

He got doctors and nurses to help, and many of the crippled boys and girls got quite better. And all over the land people got to love and trust him. He was still partly crippled—and always would be—but when the time came to choose a new President the people chose him.

It was a great honour, and it called for a great deal of hard work, but he never thought about himself as he went smiling on his way. And he led his people well, and was a good, brave President right to the very end.

The boy on the edge of the crowd in Grosvenor Square that day remembered these things; and he said to the people who couldn't puzzle out why that statue of the President had been made standing instead of sitting: 'I guess I know why. When those who knew him and loved him came to remember him, they couldn't think of him any other way than bravely standing up to things.'

And that was a very good answer. As for himself, I

think ever after, when things were hard, he would remember the brave President, and along with him a text in the New Testament: 'Stand up; I myself also am a man!' (Acts 10^{26}).

27

THE LIFE-BOAT MEN

Isn't it nice to snuggle down in bed and feel safe, when the rains and stormy winds are beating on the window-panes?

But it is not easy to do that if you live on the Isle of Wight. The boys and girls who live on the Isle of Wight are not able to forget those who must go out into the storm and battle for their lives. Never do they forget them, not even when the days are sunny and calm, and the skies are blue and beautiful.

It is quite a little island—its greatest length only twenty-three and a half miles, its width thirteen. It has chalk cliffs running steeply down to the sea, and pleasant places to swim and to tie up boats. With beautiful green downs, and shops and houses and churches, it is a lovely place, when the sun is shining and the sky is blue.

But when the storms come and hammer at the window-panes, and blow round the chimney-pots, it is different altogether. Then the life-boat men have to go out into the storm.

Beside the castle is the life-boat station. And posted up there is a thrilling list of all the calls answered by the life-boat. Sometimes the record is only of 'assistance given'; but a boy or a girl can read there also how many people were saved from the sea when their ships were wrecked. And those are the kind of brave deeds that make a lump come into your throat when you think about them, especially when the storms are battering against the window-panes.

Not long ago a Greek ship got into difficulties off some dangerous rocks near by, called 'The Needles'. But the brave life-boat men got out to her before she became a

total wreck, and thirty-seven of her seamen were brought
safely ashore.

Once, another life-boat used to be kept round on the
south side of the Island. Major Jack Seely, who lived
above that stormy coast, was her coxswain. And he has
collected many stories of the brave life-boat men who
made up her crew. He called them *The Men Who Never
Turn Back*. Isn't that a wonderful name? That is a name
we should all like to earn.

Jesus said something about people who look back and
change their minds (Luke 9⁶²). He said there is no room
in any team, or in any one crew, for one who is not whole-
hearted.

28

THE OLD PARSON'S PUDDING

ONCE there was an old parson called Archdeacon Denison. Everybody who knew him loved him, especially the boys and girls. He preached at East Brent, England, in a beautiful church with a tower and a spire. And though that was a long time ago, still today people remember him at harvest time.

From all over the countryside they gather in the beautiful church, with its tower and its spire that can be seen for miles around. Inside the church are ancient and glorious windows with Bible pictures in them in all the loveliest colours. And the church has a lovely ceiling, too, with a design like the crown of thorns that Jesus wore. At harvest time, besides flowers, there are sheaves of golden corn, and fruits—the very best and sweetest.

But the biggest excitement of all is the Harvest pudding. It all began with the old parson during the fifty-one years that he lived in East Brent, loving God's people and serving Him there.

At first one pudding was enough—and a lovely, rich, tasty pudding it was. But soon there were more and more people, especially more and more boys and girls, and so more and more puddings had to be made.

Sometimes as many as 1,400 people sat down to lunch and tea, while a band, playing joyful music, led a procession carrying a great cheese weighing ninety pounds, a big crusted loaf five feet long, and fifty plum puddings.

A wonderful Harvest Festival! No wonder the boys and girls sang their thanks that day!

Nobody knows for sure whether Paul, who wrote a lot of the letters in our New Testament, liked puddings or not, but we know that he wrote to a young friend: 'God giveth us richly all things to enjoy' (1 Timothy 6^{17}).

That would be the easiest text in the world to remember at East Brent wouldn't it?—with all those Harvest puddings; and it is good for us all to remember as we bow our heads a moment to say a grace.

To bring but one pudding to our table—not to speak of fifty—God needs the help of many people. First, there's the flour. It comes to us from the grocer, and the grocer gets it from the miller. And behind the miller are the grain farmers, and behind them, the men who prepare the land, and sow the seed, and wait for it to grow and ripen all through the long months, and harvest it in the hot golden days of late summer. And that is not to forget the men in the factory who made the plough, or the tractor, of the man whose farm it is, or the man long before who first cleared it of weeds and fenced it round.

Then there is the golden butter—and the shop and the dairy, and the butter-maker, and the dairy-farmer, and the milker, and the cow. There are eggs. And our pudding isn't made yet. God must give us some sugar—it wouldn't be nice without sugar. And mostly that has to come from hot tropical countries, away across the sea. And God needs a lot of people in those countries to plant it, and grow it, and cut it, and mill it. Then He needs ships to bring it to us.

The cows that helped with butter, have to help with milk to mix up all these good things; and then come the essences, and the currents and peel and raisins, from more sunny lands. And last of all, somebody has to make a bowl in which to mix the pudding, and a stove to cook it, and a plate to serve it on.

We cannot know for sure, whether Paul liked puddings —the old parson in East Brent did, and we do. But we can all say a big 'Thank You' to God who 'giveth us richly all things to enjoy'.

29

KNOCKING AT THE DOOR OF THE LITTLE HOUSE

SOMETIMES—and not only in fairy-stories—kings and queens and princes love to leave their palaces, and go among their people. Often their people wait for them, and wave their hats for joy. But it isn't always like that.

Once, long ago, on a cold wintry night, a traveller made his way into a little village near Moscow. He was ragged, and he longed above everything for some place to shelter him. Hungry, he made his way from door to door, begging food and a night's rest.

Now the village was very poor, and most had nothing to share. But at the very end of it there was a little house with a plain wooden door. It was poor like all the others, but there was something about it that stirred hope in the heart of the traveller. And he stopped and knocked.

Soon he could hear movement within, and next moment the door was opened by a poor villager. His clothes showed that he and his family had little to share, yet there was a look of kindness on his face.

'Come in, and welcome', said he, and he drew the weary, hungry man in. 'You will see we are poor', he said, 'and my wife is sick; but you shall have a share of all we have. We can offer you no better bed than a place on the floor, but you are welcome to that.'

Their simple meal shared, soon the family and their guest settled to their night's rest.

Early in the morning, at the breaking of the day, they all rose refreshed, and the traveller made ready to go on his way. 'I must get as far as the great city of Moscow, today', he said. And after a pause, 'I know a great man there, who has not only gold in plenty, but a kind heart like your own. Straightaway, when I get to the city, I shall seek him out. This good deed of yours shall not be forgotten.'

It all sounded too good to be more than a dream.

That night, as the little family finished their supper, and the boys and girls prepared for bed, there came another knock on their door. At first their father hesitated, but it came again. 'Who can it be?' he asked, as he rose to draw the bolt and open the door.

There on the threshold this time stood no poor traveller, but the Czar of all the Russians, Ivan the Good. And he carried in his hand a bag of gold pieces.

When the poor father and mother and their boys and girls saw him, they could hardly believe their eyes. Suddenly they knew that the poor traveller of the night before had been this same man; the highest and greatest in the land, come amongst his people. And their eyes shone with a great wonder.

In the New Testament is an even more surprising story of One higher and greater by far than Ivan the Good. It says of Him: 'He came unto His own.' But His welcome was not always so kind. In Bethlehem there was no room for Him in the inn, and when He came to His own village people, with the good news of God, they cast Him out. The New Testament says: 'He came unto His own, and His own received Him not.' But it doesn't end there: it has a happy ending, for it says, 'But as many as received Him, to them gave He power to become the sons of God' (John 1^{11-12}).

And that's still true. He will not give us handfuls of gold, as Ivan the Good did to the peasant, but He will give us something better: the true gold of happiness.

30

THE YOUNG DISCOVERER

It's always fun to hear exciting stories of discovery.

Young Albert Ellis was a discoverer. He worked in an office in Sydney. And in that office there was a door propped open by a big piece of rock. Nobody took much notice of it. It served its purpose well, and stood there getting more and more dusty.

But young Albert Ellis had eyes for seeing what nobody else could see. Day after day, as he went in and out, he spared a glance for that old door-stopper. Then he asked: 'Where did it come from? How long has it been propping open the door?'

Nobody could tell him much, save that it came from a little island lapped by the warm blue seas, away up on the Equator, called Nauru Island. That was all.

'It looks interesting', said young Albert Ellis.

Then he chipped a piece off the old door-stopper, and took it to be tested.

And when the result came, there was great excitement. Instead of the old door-stopper being just a piece of rock, good for nothing, it was a piece of high-grade phosphate. Phosphate was needed badly just then—to be crushed up and spread on thousands of acres of farm-lands, to make them good and green—and nobody knew where to get it.

Soon, very excited, young Albert Ellis was on his way through the blue seas to Nauru Island. And he discovered there lots and lots more, and on nearby Ocean Island, still more. It was all very important.

In time, news of his discovery reached the King—and he made him a Knight of the Realm, Sir Albert Ellis.

Lots and lots of ships, of course, had passed by those little islands since the old days of the pirates, flying the

Jolly Roger, the Black Flag, or no flag at all. But no one had ever discovered before that each was really a treasure island. Lots of people had passed by that old door-stopper, too, but no one had ever noticed it specially. Only a discoverer could do that, one with eyes to see what nobody else could see.

And the world still needs discoverers.

Jesus was the world's greatest Discoverer—finding what nobody guessed was there, in the hearts of people. There was Zachæus, who climbed up a tree. Everybody said he was a mean little thief, collecting taxes from people. But Jesus saw in him something fine and good. There was Mary Magdalene. Everybody said she was a bad woman. But Jesus discovered in her a heart so loving and true, that she was last at His cross, and first to meet Him on Easter morning. And there was Peter the fisherman, making his promises so easily, in whom Jesus discovered a heart so strong and true, that He nicknamed him 'the Rock man'.

Jesus needs lots of us to be discoverers, to go about the world—*and bring to light good things that nobody else dreams are here.*

31

CHARLIE'S TREES

LITTLE Charlie Goring loved trees. He loved to look at them, he loved to climb up into them. And his favourite tree began with the letter B. Can you guess what it was? He liked oaks, with their strong limbs; and he was fond of chestnuts, especially when the ripe nuts were ready to be roasted; and he loved tall poplars on the edge of the lake where he lived.

But his favourite tree was a beech—B for beech. In the spring the first new leaves were a lovely soft green, edged with tiny white downy hairs. In the summer their leafy branches gave friendly shade, and in the Autumn when their leaves turned to many colours, they were just as lovely.

Wiston House—pronounced Wisson—where Charlie Goring lived, was a happy old house. In the lake, just before it, were lots of trout. Occasionally wild duck came there. Sometimes a heron might be seen.

Everything at Wiston House Charlie loved; but the trees were his special friends. Every day as he looked out, he could see just beyond them, a great bare slope. To Charlie it seemed very high, and very bare, and very ugly. And as he looked, a wish was born in his heart. 'Wouldn't it be lovely', he said to himself, 'if that great bare slope could have a ring of trees round the top? Besides being beautiful, they would serve as a landmark to guide the people who are always getting lost on the downs.' When Charlie thought of trees, he thought, of course, of beeches—lovely in spring, summer, autumn, winter, lovely all the year round.

Year after year Charlie kept thinking about his wish. One day he climbed to the top of the bare slope, and planted a little tree. Soon, beside it, he planted another, and then another and another. Some people laughed and said: 'The wind will blow them down. In any case, it will take years and years before they are big.'

But Charlie didn't mind. He loved his little beech trees, and he went on planting them until he had a ring right round the top. Day after day he gave them his care. And the wind did not blow them down, and soon they were as tall as himself. In time they were taller—and every day as Charlie looked up from Wiston House, he rejoiced in them. By this time, of course, people had long given up their teasing, because that bare, ugly place had become one of the beauty-spots of England—called Chanctonbury Ring.

And to this day, lots of boys and girls, and lots of big people, too, go there to rejoice in the shade and beauty of Charlie's beech trees. And they always come away refreshed.

When Charlie became an old white-haired man, he wrote a little poem after he had looked up and seen his beautiful beeches on Chanctonbury Ring. And this is what he said, in his happy poem, full of thanksgiving:

> How oft around thy Ring, sweet Hill,
>   A boy, I used to play,
> And form my plans to plant thy top
>   On some auspicious day.
>
> And then an almost hopeless wish
>   Would creep within my breast,
> Oh! could I live to see thy top
>   In all its beauty dress'd.
>
> That time's arrived: I've had my wish,
>   And lived to eighty-five;
> I'll thank my God who gave such grace
>   As long as e'er I live.

And many others now thank God that Charlie got his wish, but most of all, that he had the patience and courage to start something good and beautiful in the world, though he knew it would take a long time.